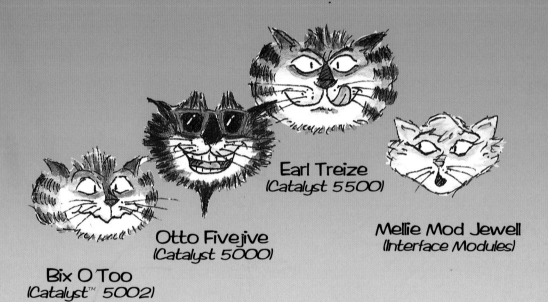

Earl Treize
(Catalyst 5500)

Otto Fivejive
(Catalyst 5000)

Mellie Mod Jewell
(Interface Modules)

Bix O Too
(Catalyst™ 5002)

The Scalable ~~Tale~~ Tail of the Intranet Cats

CiscoFusion™: Scaling the Intranet

True Plug & Play

Plug any of the attached Cisco interface modules into any Cisco Catalyst 5000 series switch.

Cisco Systems, Inc.
170 West Tasman Drive
San Jose, CA 95134-1706 USA

Telephone: 408 526-4000
800 553-NETS (6387)
Fax: 408 526-4100
World Wide Web URL:
http://www.cisco.com

The Scalable Tale of the Intranet Cats

*A Scalable Fable and a
Just-in-time Rhyme*

'Twas the night before the big day that Ned was to star
At a mega presentation where he could go far
If he could tell management they had no networking woes
And that their Intranet would help them outperform their foes.

He needed to find solutions that would fill all with glee
And make every aspect of their network seem ultra easy.
Oh, how could he deal with this problem humungo
And find his way out of this labyrinthian jungle?
Despondent and dejected, he felt overtaken by fatigue,
Finding comfort in sleep and dreams of Little League.

But oh so rudely he suddenly awoke with a jump
As he heard from the closet a very loud thump...
Then a squeak and a squeal and a heck of a hiss—
The sounds of battle rattled, echoed and this
Was what prompted Ned to go open the door
To the wiring closet from which the noises did pour.

And the minute he did, his eyes saucers became
As he spied a fat cat chasing out rats who were lame
"Out of my house, you outdated hubs,
No more freeloading here, no more rub-a-dub-dubs!"

Seeing Ned, the cat smiled and thrust out a paw
Doing his best to stifle a tiny guffaw.
"You must be Ned—we're roommates so to speak.
I'm Otto Fivejive and lest you think I'm a geek—
I'm a feisty feline and a mighty cool cat—
It's my job and my pleasure to get rid of every hub-rat."

"When you hang out with us cats, relegate to a myth
Ye old contention that there's never enough bandwidth
For your users to video-communicate and connect to data
Your job becomes so easy, you can say 'See ya lata!'"

"That's right," boomed a voice, a veritable basso profundo
So velvety rich, so robust and rotundo,
That Ned spun around in a tornado-like whirl
To find himself greeted by: "Glad to meet you, I'm Earl."

Otto said, "Earl's my cousin, power and speed he's got;
Limited to the old ways he is most definitely *not*!
VLAN capable, he can take you where no one has tread.
On his shoulders he wears a high-IQ head.
He effortlessly enables the multicast you desire
Without having to determine which priority is higher."

Ned envisioned how happy his users (and bosses) will be.
"Best of all, they'll be productive and never need to see
How I've accomplished all this, transparent it shall stay
Hallelujah—at last—it'll be a new day!"

"Wait, there's one more kitty to deploy in a financial fix,"
With this intriguing intro, Otto alluded to Bix:
"This practical cat offers an affordable migration path,
He's interoperable with the rest of us; much value he hath."

After making the acquaintance of the cadre of Cisco cats
And watching them get rid of more pesky hub-rats,
Ned sighed in relief about scalability that breaks old rules...
Plus redundant supervisors and dual-sharing tools.
All this is but the beginning as past limits fade to black;
In this new era, Networking Ned will nothing lack.

In closing, let us remind you once more of the score
How Cisco can help you and your Intranet soar!

13

Our cats deliver on the promise of CiscoFusion™
That the customer is king is no longer mere illusion!
So follow us on our smooth-as-silk migration path;
See for yourself how our modular solution, it hath
Scalability galore...manageability and more—
Delivering ease of use today...plus plug and play!

The Catalyst™ 5000 family lets you finally create
A next-generation switched infrastructure to interoperate.
Before you know, you'll be ahead of the game
As you master the jungle...and wild networking beasts tame.

Our tale reveals what we've done is simply heed
Your feedback about what you truly do need.
Now before we move on to detail our family of cats,
Let us salute the customer; let us take off our hats.
Kudos, congrats...thanks a mill,
Without *you* our efforts mean zero, zip and nil!

The end of our Tale *Tail*
Just the beginning...

Scaling the Intranet with the Catalyst 5000 Family

Enter the Era of Intranets

**With So Much Riding on Your Intranet,
High Performance Is Imperative**

In a very short time, the corporate Intranet has become essential to the everyday business process at most large companies.

It has become a vital conduit of corporate communication and information, as the entire process of doing business is being put on the Intranet—everything from internal engineering tasks, documentation, all manner of databases...right through to external communications such as advertising, product literature, customer services, and support.

These corporate Intranets have greatly changed the way companies do business, bringing with them both benefits and challenges. Now, not only do users turn to their Web browsers to access information or communicate with each other via sophisticated applications via the Internet, they are increasingly relying on their company's Intranet.

It's now common to see Web browser software on every desktop. Users count on their Intranets to send multimedia mail, air video over IP, conduct computer-based training, engage in desktop conferencing, and so on. The good news is that businesses may run more efficiently, but the bad news is that if the system goes down—there goes productivity.

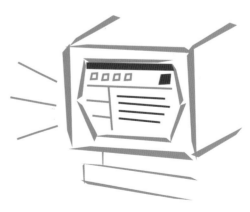

With the emergence of this pervasive new set of Intranet applications, several major changes are occurring in campus networks that are a direct result of the changing nature of how applications use the network:

- **Traffic Growth:** New network-enabled Intranet applications are causing an exponential increase in network traffic.

- **Convergence on Unified Application Model:** This convergence complicates any attempts to separate mission-critical traffic from other Intranet traffic through existing classification mechanisms.

- **Reduced Locality of Traffic:** With the ad hoc nature of Intranet communications, the ratio of traffic switched within a workgroup to that crossing the backbone can no longer be optimized to 80% local and 20% nonlocal. This diminishing locality has resulted in increased campus-wide traffic, stressing campus backbones. In fact, this ratio is probably closer now to 50:50 in most campus networks, and may actually invert, 20:80, at which point campus backbones can become seriously congested.

What's the Solution?

Faced with these new requirements, network administrators are constructing scalable switched networks to provide high performance and quality delivery of Intranet applications.

New Solutions to Meet New Requirements

Cisco Systems has the right combination of high-performance, affordable hardware, and industry-leading software to deliver a new set of scalable services for the Intranet. What are these services?

A solid network infrastructure does require certain foundation network services. You need to future-proof your network with **scalability services**. You want your infrastructure to be fast and efficient with the appropriate **connectivity services.** You want to optimize your network investment with the right **management services**, so you know what's going on in your network and can spot trouble before disaster strikes. And of course, you want to protect your priceless information with the right **security services**. Know who your users are and what they're doing! And last, but not least, you want a reliable network that works. No excuses.

Beyond the basic enabled services, the new campus Intranet also requires a set of value-added services to deliver information and applications in a timely and qualitative fashion to every desktop. Without these mechanisms available on the Intranet, applications like video, audio, and other interactive applications become slow, unpredictable, and often useless.

Cisco's Campus Intranet Services

Value-Added Network Services	Multimedia/Multicast
	Class of Service
	Mobility Services

Enabled Network Services	Scalability Services
	Connectivity Services
	Management Services
	Security Services
	Reliability Services

Follow this color coding throughout the book...

A Scalable Solution to Suit Your Every Intranet Need

A Quick Overview

The CiscoFusion™ architecture for scalable switched campus Intranets provides the performance of switching with proven, value-added features.

CiscoFusion provides a framework of eight Intranet Services with real deliverables that customers can rely upon based on Cisco Internetwork Operating System (Cisco IOS™) software. Cisco Intranet services solve key problems to address the growing challenges of building scalable Intranets.

Cisco's Solutions to Intranet Problems

Scalability Problem:
The traditional model of high-speed switched LANs interconnecting routers and servers no longer applies. Random communication between Web-based clients and servers independent of location demands scalable performance for all users spanning both switched and routed networks.

Scalability Solution:
Cisco offers all the scalability of routing at the speed and with the simplicity of switching, using distributed NetFlow™ switching and Tag Switching for large Intranets and Internets.

Connectivity Problem:
Traffic growth and new Intranet applications are causing exponential increase in network traffic, demanding wire-speed performance across the campus. Users are faced with ever increasing technology options with the promise of Gigabit switching rates.

Connectivity Solution:
The Catalyst 5000 series switches deliver the needed performance on a single scalable platform. Cisco supports all multiprotocol desktop and enterprise internetworking requirements with the widest range of VLAN and media support including Fast EtherChannel™, Gigabit Ethernet, and ATM.

Management Problem:
Managing large switched Intranets requires a balanced solution of plug-and-play, flexibility, and control over network availability and performance.

Management Solution:
The combination of intelligent agent technology, proxy management, embedded RMON, and application-specific tools provides campus-wide Intranet manageability.

Security Problem:

With the inherent requirement for mission-critical campus Intranets, there is a growing need for end-to-end security consistent with enterprise-wide security policies.

Security Solution:

Cisco provides consistent authentication and access control across switches and routers, including secure port filtering, permissions through policy management, inter-VLAN firewall services, and enterprise security management.

Reliability Problem:

Running mission-critical applications over the campus Intranet requires consistent network reliability, availability, and redundancy.

Reliability Solution:

Cisco offers a set of reliability services delivering end-to-end network availability across the campus Intranet. These include link device and network redundancy. The network works—no excuses.

Multimedia/Multicast Problem:

One of the most effective ways to communicate information to employees and customers is via interactive multimedia. Applications such as video over IP and PointCast drive the need for new, networked multimedia solutions. These new multicast-intensive applications require switches and routers to efficiently handle broadcast-intensive traffic.

Multimedia/Multicast Solution:

Cisco now delivers end-to-end multicast support across all routers and switches on the campus Intranet. This service forwards traffic only to those switch users who subscribe to individual multicast groups without impacting all other users.

Class of Service Problem:

With the convergence of mission-critical business and multimedia applications on the campus Intranet, there is an increasing need for Class of Service to prioritize important business applications over other applications.

Class of Service Solution:

Cisco delivers multiple mechanisms to bring CoS/QoS to the desktop, both over ATM and LAN switching. Embedded across our switches and routers are technology options, including RSVP, IP precedence, CGMP, and ABR.

Mobility Problem:

In today's dynamic business environment, users continually move around the corporate network. Users moving within the Intranet present daunting challenges for network planners, including network addressing and name management, switch and VLAN configuration management, and scaling performance at different access points across the Intranet.

Mobility Solution:

Cisco solves the mobility problem with dynamic addressing using Dynamic Host Configuration Protocol (DHCP) and Domain Name Services (DNS), along with flexible VLAN services and distributed NetFlow switching for optimal scalable performance, regardless of location.

Cisco's Campus Intranet Services

Building a Scalable, High-Performance Intranet Infrastructure

Scaling the Intranet with CiscoFusion

To accommodate the growing demands for networking bandwidth, scalability, and redundancy, you need to deploy a high-performance, cost-effective, and manageable network. Cisco Systems offers a set of powerful Intranet solutions that will help you evolve from a shared-media network to a switched network, while protecting your existing investment in your network infrastructure.

The CiscoFusion architecture incorporates LAN switching within the wiring closet and multilayer switching and routing on the backbone, enabling you to incrementally add exactly the amount of bandwidth, intelligent traffic control, and management required to best serve the needs of your network.

Embedded within each platform is our value-added Cisco IOS software. This software provides the linkages between all Cisco devices in the Intranet infrastructure that allows them to interoperate seamlessly and enables them to meet the requirements of these Intranet applications.

CiscoFusion: Scaling the Intranet

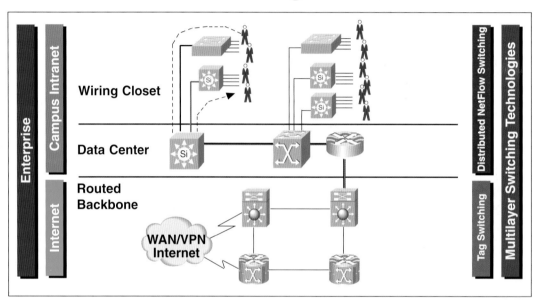

For more detailed information on the CiscoFusion architecture, please refer to the CiscoFusion White Paper on Cisco Connection Online:

http://www.cisco.com.

Cisco's Enabled Intranet Services

A solid network infrastructure requires solid **enabled network services**...

Exactamente, Ned. That's why Cisco provides **scalability services** *to futureproof your network.*

We also offer **connectivity services** for speed and efficiency...and **management services** to optimize your network investment.

Plus, our **security services** help you protect sensitive, priceless info. And none of this matters one iota if you don't have **reliability services**.

Scalability Services

The amount of network traffic per user has skyrocketed over the last three years. The primary reason for more Intranet traffic is not just more users, but increased traffic from Web-based applications, larger file transfers, and new multimedia/multicast application activity. The 80:20 rule is now inverting and "any-to-any" communication requires both Layer 2 and Layer 3 performance and scalability.

In order to meet these changing traffic patterns and application requirements, higher-performance Layer 3 forwarding becomes essential. In addition, as enterprises scale their networks by moving to gigabit interfaces, it is essential to move the forwarding functionality from software-based distributed switching to ASIC hardware to achieve media speed Layer 3 switching. Cisco addresses this requirement as part of CiscoFusion with distributed NetFlow switching.

Distributed NetFlow switching is a key component of the CiscoFusion architecture for providing media-speed Layer 3 switching across the Catalyst 5000 and 5500 series switches product line. It combines the performance of Layer 2 switching platforms along with the functionality of the Cisco IOS software. Using silicon-based Layer 3 switching technology allows distributed NetFlow switching to scale to millions of packets per second for tomorrow's next-generation gigabit technologies, providing unprecedented price/performance.

Distributed NetFlow switching capabilities not only drive throughput by adding routing intelligence to routine switching tasks, they also help keep track of what's going on in the network with sophisticated accounting features.

- **Distributed NetFlow switching** will be achieved by upgrading the new feature card on the Catalyst 5000 series. This feature card concept also exists on the ATM switch processor. Having the ability to upgrade switch hardware as Cisco adds new features and performance to the Catalyst 5000 series is a key advantage to achieve scalability while protecting the investment customers make in the Catalyst 5000 series.

Distributed NetFlow Switching

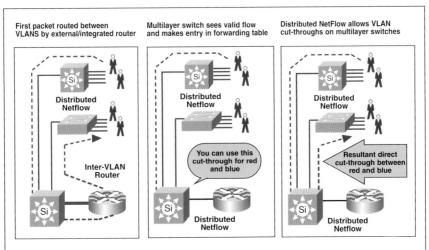

First packet routed between VLANS by external/integrated router

Multilayer switch sees valid flow and makes entry in forwarding table

Distributed NetFlow allows VLAN cut-throughs on multilayer switches

- **The new route/switch module** for the Catalyst 5000 series will bring integrated support for Layer 3 and high touch services, leveraging Cisco 7500 technology. More importantly, it will add Cisco IOS routing functionality to the platform without impacting the Layer 2 switching performance.

The combination of these two powerful new elements for the Catalyst 5000 series will enable customers to scale Layer 3 forwarding rates throughout the switched infrastructure while maintaining central control and security through Cisco IOS software on existing routers or the new integrated router/switch modules.

Bringing VLANs to a large-scale network solves the problem of broadcast containment and security on a Layer 2 switched network. Inter-VLAN connectivity is done with routing and distributed NetFlow switching. Cisco's VLAN architecture is the most advanced, scalable VLAN solution available.

Connectivity Services

High-performance and scalable connectivity is crucial to successful Intranet services. In the Catalyst family, Cisco offers the greatest range of media interfaces along with a high-performance, nonblocking switch architecture that sends your traffic through.

The award-winning Catalyst 5000 platform has been extended to include two new chassis and a host of greater connectivity options for higher port density and incredible performance. Here's what *Data Communications* had to say about the Catalyst 5000 platform when they tested it: "The performance of Cisco's Catalyst 5000 was astounding—it took top honors in every test. Searching for some weakness somewhere, we deliberately subjected the unit to a 200 percent overload on all ports for three minutes. It didn't drop a frame. For best performance...this is the box to buy."

The Catalyst 5500 Series Switches

The new Catalyst 5500 platform combines cell and frame switching and routing into a single chassis for the first time from Cisco. It's designed from the ground up to connect and perform as your traffic load increases with superior buffering and congestion control. Thirteen slots and separate frame and cell supervisors share a common backplane; the Catalyst 5500 can scale to hundreds of ports and up to 50 gigabits of total switching capacity—for performance of tens of millions packets per second!

The Catalyst 5002 Series Switches

The new Catalyst 5002 platform puts Catalyst 5000 power in a small package, with full-feature multilayer frame switching capability in a two slot chassis. With the same one million packets per second switching fabric as the award-winning Catalyst 5000, the Catalyst 5002 switch is ideal for specific connectivity requirements for smaller wiring closet, workgroup, and backbone applications.

The Catalyst 5000 Series Switches

The award-winning Catalyst 5000 platform with a five-slot chassis and frame-switching fabric switches up to one million packets per second and never misses a beat. Upgrading to the new Supervisor Engine II enhances performance even more.

Cisco leads the way with new media options for the Catalyst 5000 family. The Catalyst 5500 switch is ready for Gigabit Ethernet and high-speed ATM switching. New Fast EtherChannel technology increases Fast Ethernet uplink bandwidth capacity four to eight times with support for multiple virtual LAN per Fast EtherChannel. Fast EtherChannel is the grouping of multiple Fast Ethernet interfaces into one logical transmission path to provide parallel bandwidth between switches, servers, or Cisco routers.

For frame-based backbone connectivity, the Catalyst 5000 series includes support for Fast Ethernet, Fast EtherChannel, and Gigabit Ethernet. And for cell-based backbone connectivity, this platform also supports ATM, OC-3, and OC-12 links.

Scaling the Intranet from a connectivity perspective means tackling the price/performance issues of widespread switched network deployment with greater port density and more switching capacity.

As the price/performance leader, Cisco has added all this new capacity to the Catalyst platform at a very competitive price. The price per port of shared media modular hubs has remained stable over the last two years, while Cisco has driven the per-port price of switched 10BaseT Ethernet down to approaching that of a modular hub. Switched Ethernet now offers ten times the performance of a hub at about the same price, making migration more attractive than ever.

Cisco: Switched Ethernet at Shared Ethernet Prices

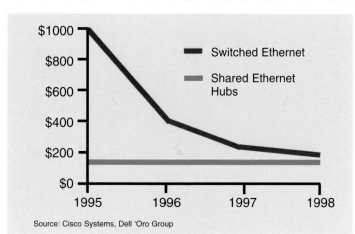

Source: Cisco Systems, Dell 'Oro Group

Management Services

Your Intranet is a substantial investment and a complex interaction of technologies. You need centralized, easy-to-use management tools to optimize your investment performance and manage it as efficiently as possible.

When creating the right management software, Cisco realized that moving from shared to switched media requires enhanced visibility to devices, traffic, and end-users. Cisco Catalyst switches are intelligent devices with agents embedded in the switch fabric. These agents maintain traffic visibility and provide views of the physical network, VLAN management for displaying VLAN management groups, and end-user trace utilities for locating end-users.

Current network management tools only examine networks at a device level, with limited topology information. These tools are usually reactive, meaning that they help you find and solve problems that already exist.

Cisco is developing a policy-based management system that proactively manages from a broad, network-wide perspective. These new tools will enforce IS-defined policies to achieve business-oriented goals of performance, security, and availability.

CiscoFusion Management Architecture

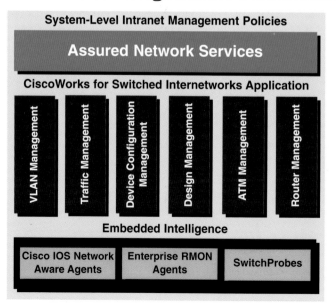

CiscoWorks for Switched Internetworks:
An Evolving Platform that Maps into the CiscoFusion Architecture

CiscoWorks for Switched Internetworks has several tools that work in tandem for a powerful, proactive approach to network management. Powerful offline network analysis tools from the NETSYS product line let managers test network configurations for possible failure points or try out new configurations before deploying them on the live network.

CiscoWorks for Switched Internetworks creates end-to-end integrated manageability for switched networks. It operates from a network management server in the data center with Web-based distributed access, and features an array of tightly integrated management, monitoring, and configuration tools.

Current and soon-to-come management tools perform VLAN configuration and management, traffic analysis, campus design analysis, device configuration, ATM device and service management, and user authentication and reporting.

CiscoWorks for Switched Internetworks

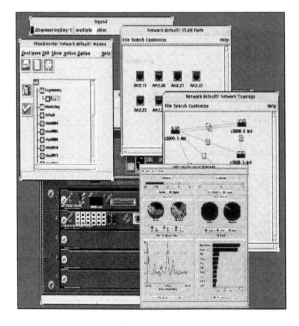
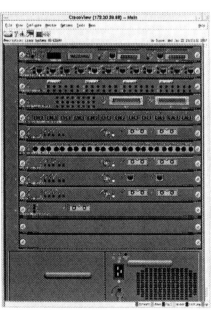

Security Services

With the size and complexity of an enterprise network, it's more important than ever to apply and administer a consistent security policy from end-to-end. The Cisco enterprise security architecture combines existing and new Cisco IOS-based technologies and security products to ensure a complete and uniform solution that enables enterprises to enforce a security policy.

As part of the Catalyst 5000 series solutions, Cisco supports secure port filtering and policy-based access control lists, which protect devices from configuration changes and intrusion.

Secure port filtering lets switches automatically block unwelcome access to sensitive data by shutting down a port. Should traffic from an unauthorized MAC address try to penetrate a protected port, it will automatically disable the port and send an alarm to the central management console.

Network device authentication tools, such as TACACS+, allow for secure access to any switch configuration information, while Syslog keeps track of any configuration changes on the Catalyst 5000 switches.

Intranet Security

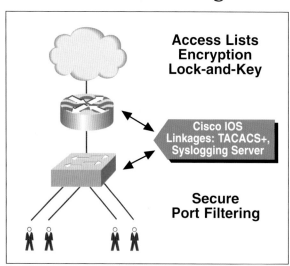

Access Lists
Encryption
Lock-and-Key

Cisco IOS
Linkages: TACACS+,
Syslogging Server

Secure
Port Filtering

Reliability Services

Y̵ou're running mission-critical applications over your Intranet. Your network must be up and running: users expect it and revenue depends on it. A reliable network works—no excuses.

Cisco Intranet solutions have many features that guarantee reliability. The Catalyst hardware is designed for redundancy, with dual load-sharing power supplies, optional redundant Supervisor Engines, physical link redundancy, and fully hot-swappable, functional components.

Redundant links between switches and routers are supported using Fast EtherChannel load-sharing and physical link redundancy. If one link fails, the other automatically takes the entire traffic load. Link redundancy is also provided through dual redundant connectors on high-speed backbone links.

Cisco IOS software supports resilience with VLAN trunk link redundancy and load sharing. The ATM LAN Emulation server uses Simple Server Redundancy Protocol (SSRP) to support distributed or redundant LAN Emulation services.

Hot Standby Router Protocol (HSRP) coordinates automatic rerouting of traffic around a primary router failure.

Intranet Reliability

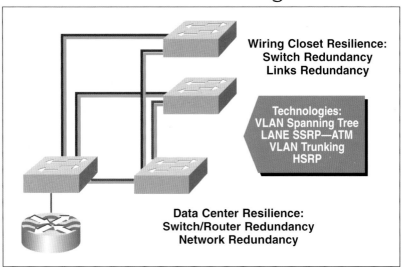

Wiring Closet Resilience:
Switch Redundancy
Links Redundancy

Technologies:
VLAN Spanning Tree
LANE SSRP—ATM
VLAN Trunking
HSRP

Data Center Resilience:
Switch/Router Redundancy
Network Redundancy

Value-Added Intranet Services

Multimedia/Multicast Services

Cisco supports multimedia applications with nonblocking, media-speed switching across all Catalyst platforms. Applications that include voice and video take advantage of multicast technologies.

Embedded in the Cisco IOS software on all Cisco switches and routers, Cisco Group Membership Protocol (CGMP) on the Catalyst 5000 series switches prevents multicast flooding. CGMP allows wire-speed multicast handling on the Catalyst 5000 via a software upgrade to the existing Supervisor Engine. It also prevents the flooding of IP multicast packets among all switched ports within a VLAN. CGMP relies on a Cisco router to download the identity of the multicast clients within the switched network to the Catalyst 5000 Supervisor Engine. Using this Layer 3 information, the Supervisor then programs the switching engine to switch these multicast packets at full line rates to only those ports interested in this traffic.

CGMP is the first of many Layer 3 enhancements that will provide value-added functionality and tighter integration between Cisco Catalyst switches and traditional, router-based Cisco IOS software components.

Scalable Multimedia Support

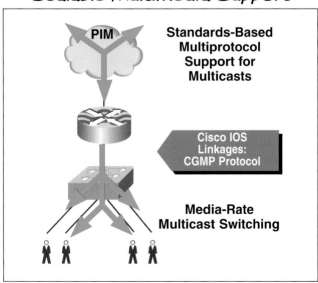

Class of Service

Now that you're transporting voice, video, and data over the same network, you have to implement Class of Service, or the ability to keep time-sensitive activities moving in your network.

Cisco will leverage CGMP to deliver Resource Reservation Protocol (RSVP) to port priority mappings on the Catalyst 5000 platforms, delivering Class of Service to the desktop.

Quality of Service is similar, but specialized for ATM networks. Cisco's industry-standard Available Bit Rate (ABR) and other technologies consistently deliver the most reliable and feature-rich Quality of Service functionality in the industry.

Class of Service and Quality of Service features built into Cisco Intranet products save you money by making the best use of your bandwidth and by lowering infrastructure costs.

Intranet Class of Service

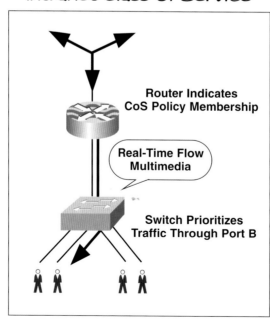

Mobility Services

User mobility across the Intranet presents three sets of challenges for network managers—management of network addresses and naming assignments, reconfiguration of devices and services such as VLANs, and optimization of traffic flows, scaling performance throughout the campus network.

Administration of network addressing for IP-based end stations requires manual configuration as users move across the Intranet. With the acceptance of Dynamic Host Configuration Protocol (DHCP) within desktop systems, the administration of IP addresses becomes simplified and dynamic. Furthermore, mapping these network addresses to end station names simplifies tracking end-users across the network. Cisco's solution to managing network addresses and host name mappings leverages global servers such as Domain Name Servers (DNS) and integrates this with DHCP servers. Cisco's CDDM Manager integrates a DHCP server for dynamic addressing with an enterprise-quality DNS server.

Reconfiguration of switch ports and VLANs is relatively simple to manage once you have embedded intelligence within the switches. This dynamically tracks VLAN mappings to ports and end-user MAC addresses. Cisco's dynamic VLAN solution across its Catalyst product line provides a mechanism to automate this configuration function for moves and changes in the network.

Finally, scalable performance across the Intranet is required for both Layer 2 and Layer 3 devices. Cisco's multilayer switching architecture, spanning both router and switch product lines, offers media-rate switching performance while maintaining control and security over inter-VLAN traffic, regardless of location.

Mobility Across the Campus Intranet

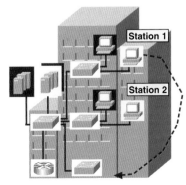

Real-World Applications

Wiring Closet Applications

We've explored how the Catalyst 5000 switch family meets or exceeds your basic and value-added network service requirements. Now it's time to consider how a Catalyst 5000 switch fits into real network applications.

The Intranet wiring closet makes or breaks a network design. Users must have performance to match usage. With the new Catalyst 5500 platform, even higher port densities make the Catalyst series a very attractive wiring closet solution at a very competitive price per port. Now cost is not an issue as you consider migrating from shared-media hubs to higher-performance switching to the desktop. New multilayer switching services make the Catalyst 5000 series even more attractive as a wiring closet switch.

The Catalyst 5000 series' nonblocking architecture ensures both performance and reliability with high throughput. A choice of switched Ethernet, Fast Ethernet, ATM, and soon Token Ring connectivity to the desktop and high-speed backbone uplinks to ATM, FDDI, Fast Ethernet, and soon Gigabit Ethernet, the Catalyst 5000 series brings many connectivity options to the wiring closet. You can now bring switched Ethernet into your wiring closet for the same price per port as a shared-media hub. That's better performance at about the same price!

Data Center Applications

In the data center, the Catalyst 5000 family has outstanding performance as a collapsed backbone switch or as a backbone switch adjacent to a high-performance router such as the Cisco 7500. As a collapsed backbone switch, a Catalyst 5500 switch can serve as a high-density Fast Ethernet backbone switch or as a powerful ATM switch, connecting multiple wiring closet switches as well as servers in the data center.

Scaling the Campus Intranet

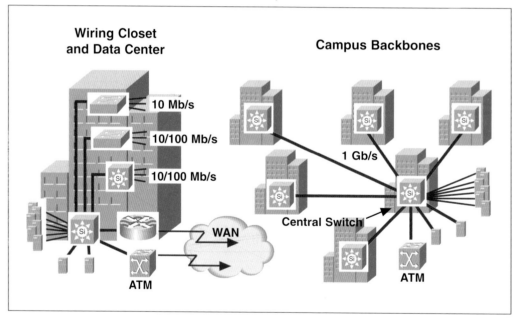

Campus Backbone Applications

The Catalyst 5000 family is a flexible, powerful backbone switch solution with full media-speed connectivity to high-speed ATM, FDDI, Fast Ethernet, and Fast EtherChannel, and soon Gigabit Ethernet.

As a campus backbone switch, the multilayer switching capability of the Catalyst family brings unprecedented performance and flexibility to the campus backbone. It enables rapid inter-VLAN service across the campus, reserving valuable router cycles for other activities such as firewall protection, Internet access, or high-speed WAN connectivity to regional offices.

The Cisco IOS software in the Catalyst 5000 family supports advanced ATM routing features such as PNNI, LAN Emulation, and traffic management for outstanding and scalable ATM performance over hundreds of switches in a campus enterprise network.

The Catalyst 5000 series switches bring new levels of scalability, flexibility, and functionality to the network. With the wide range of modules and comprehensive set of Intranet services available, the Catalyst 5000 series now effectively meets all requirements of the new campus Intranet.

Conclusion

Learn what Ned learned in our scalable fable. See for yourself how Cisco's Catalyst 5000 family of switches offers a complete set of enterprise switching solutions, spanning everything from the campus backbone to the desktop. Building on the award-winning architectures of the Catalyst 5000 and LightStream® 1010 while integrating the Cisco IOS-based routing technology in a single platform, this combination of "best-of-breed" technologies presents you with a powerful solution for building the new corporate Intranet *for today and tomorrow.*

Our cats deliver on the promise of CiscoFusion
That the customer is king is no longer mere illusion!
So follow us on our smooth-as-silk migration path;
See for yourself how our modular solution, it hath
Scalability galore...manageability and more—
Delivering ease of use today...plus plug and play!

CISCO SYSTEMS

**Cisco Systems
Corporate Headquarters
Cisco Systems, Inc.**
170 West Tasman Drive
San Jose, CA 95134-1706
USA
World Wide Web URL:
http://www.cisco.com
Tel: 408 526-4000
      800 553-NETS (6387)
Fax: 408 526-4100

European Headquarters
Cisco Systems Europe
s.a.r.l.
Parc Evolic - Batiment L1/L2
16, Avenue du Quebec
BP 706-Villebon
91961 Courtaboeuf Cedex
France
Tel: 33-1-6918-61-00
Fax: 33-1-6928-83 26

**Intercontinental
Headquarters**
Cisco Systems, Inc.
170 West Tasman Drive
San Jose, CA 95134-1706
USA
Tel: 408 526-7660
Fax: 408 526-4646

**Latin American
Headquarters**
Cisco Systems, Inc.
790 N.W. 107th Avenue
Suite 102
Miami, FL 33172
USA
Tel: 305 228-1200
Fax: 305 222-8456

Japanese Headquarters
Nihon Cisco Systems K.K.
Fuji Building
3-2-3 Marunouchi
Chiyoda-ku, Tokyo 100
Japan
Tel: 81-3-5211-2800
Fax: 81-3-5211-2810

**Cisco Systems has over 190 offices in the following countries. Addresses, phone numbers, and fax numbers are listed on
Cisco Connection Online at http://www.cisco.com.**

Argentina • Australia • Austria • Belgium • Brazil • Canada • • Chile • China (PRC) • Colombia • Costa Rica • Denmark • Finland • France • Germany
Hong Kong • India • Indonesia • Ireland • Italy • Japan • Korea • Malaysia • Mexico • The Netherlands • New Zealand • Norway • Philippines
Portugal • Singapore • South Africa • Spain • Sweden • Switzerland • Taiwan, ROC • Thailand • United Arab Emirates • United Kingdom • Venezuela

Book Concept: Wong•Wong•Boyack, San Francisco • Design & Illustration: Ben Wong • Copy: Penelope Wong, Jana Bender, Ben Wong • Production: Michael Frandy • Printing: Hanku Asia, Seoul

Earl Treize
(Catalyst 5500)

Otto Fivejive
(Catalyst 5000)

Bix O Too
(Catalyst™ 5002)

Mellie Mod Jewell
(Interface Modules)